Bastien Piano Basics

TECHNIC

PRIMER LEVEL

BY JAMES BASTIEN

Contents

*To reinforce the feeling of achievement, the teacher or student may put a √ when the page has been mastered.

ISBN 0-8497-5280-9

C Position

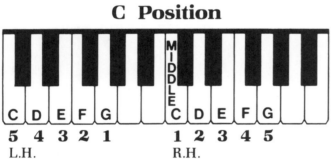

C D E F G   MIDDLE C D E F G

5 4 3 2 1   1 2 3 4 5

L.H.   R.H.

Practice Directions
1. Play evenly with curved fingers.
2. Play legato, connecting the tones smoothly.
3. Play slowly at first; play faster when you are ready.
4. Play loud or soft.

Use these same Practice Directions for pages 3-5.

C Warm-up

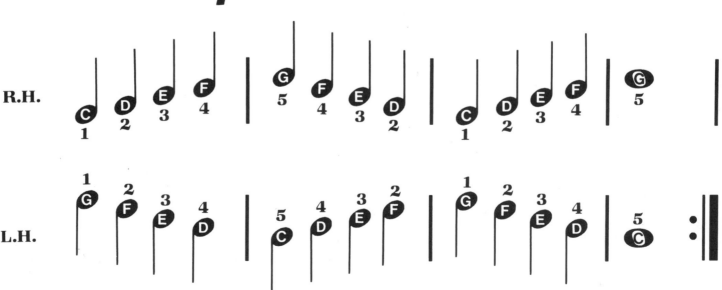

Climbing the Bars

R.H. E3 D2 C1 D2 | E3 D2 C1 D2 | E3 D2 E3 F4 | G5 |

L.H. 3E 2F 1G 2F | 3E 2F 1G 2F | 3E 2F 3E 4D | 5C :||

Teeter-Totter Fun!

R.H. C1 D2 C1 D2 | E3 D2 E3 D2 | E3 F4 E3 F4 | G5 |

L.H. 1G 2F 1G 2F | 3E 2F 3E 2F | 3E 4D 3E 4D | 5C :||

Use with page 17 of Piano, Primer Level. **WP215**

4

Sea Whale

Ocean Octopus

The Merry-Go-Round

Circus Clown

C Position

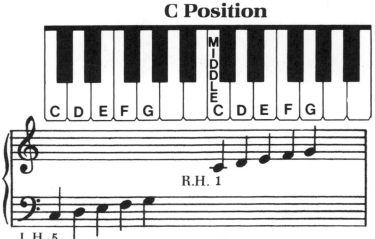

Practice Directions
1. Play evenly with curved fingers.
2. Play legato, connecting the tones smoothly.
3. Play slowly at first; play faster when you are ready.

Use these same Practice Directions for the rest of the book.

f-p means to play the first time *f* (loud), the second time *p* (soft).

Roller Coaster Ride

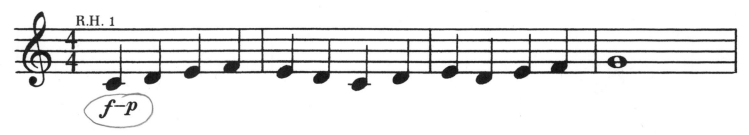

Play hands separately first.
Repeat and play hands together.*

On the Ferris Wheel

Teacher: This practice direction is only a suggestion. You may want the student to begin with both hands.

Monkey Twins

Three Giraffes

Lift your hand at the end of each slur with an "up wrist" motion. Lift on count 3.

Floating Clouds

Lift your hand at the end of each slur with an "up wrist" motion. Lift on count 4.

Lifting Balloons

A +

Observe the ties.
Lift your hand at the end
of each slur on count 4.

Tied Score

Observe the ties.
Lift your hands at the end
of each slur on count 3.

All Tied Up!

Four Crows

Use with page 36-37 of Piano, Primer Level.

Five Rabbits

Melodic Intervals

Harmonic Intervals

Use with page 39 of Piano, Primer Level.

After playing each interval twice
as written, you may then repeat
each interval three times, then
four times.

Clip-Clop Trail

Echo Canyon

Chords Are Fun!

f–p Play this chord, C's its name, Curve your fin-gers, please take aim!

*Continue this pattern up the keyboard on the white keys.

In each exercise below, play the chords softer than the melody.

Melody and Chords

1.

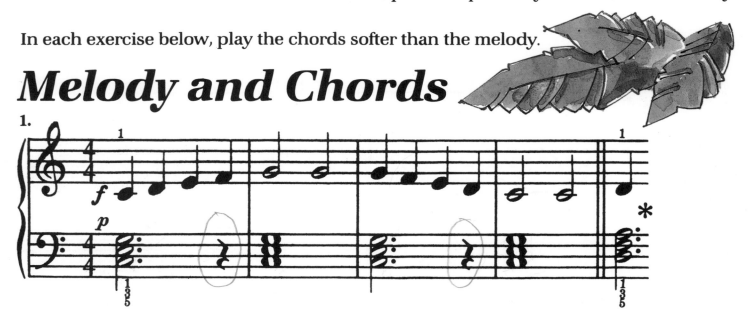

*Continue this pattern up the keyboard on the white keys.

2.

*Continue this pattern up the keyboard on the white keys.

Harp Chords

*Continue this pattern up the keyboard on the white keys.

Middle C Position

Let's Go Sliding!

*Continue this pattern up the keyboard on the white keys.

Bees in Springtime

A+

*Continue this pattern up the keyboard on the white keys.

The Crawling Caterpillar

*Continue this pattern up the keyboard on the white keys.

Use with page 46-47 of Piano, Primer Level. **WP215**

Hear the Wind Blow!

Use with pages 48-49 of Piano, Primer Level.

The Busy Windmill

G Position

R.H. 1

L.H. 5

2nds and 3rds

f-p

Hopscotch

f-p

G Chords

Boogie Time

Use with pages 54-55 of Piano, Primer Level. **WP215**

Let's Jump!

Bouncing Balls

Wooden Shoe Dance

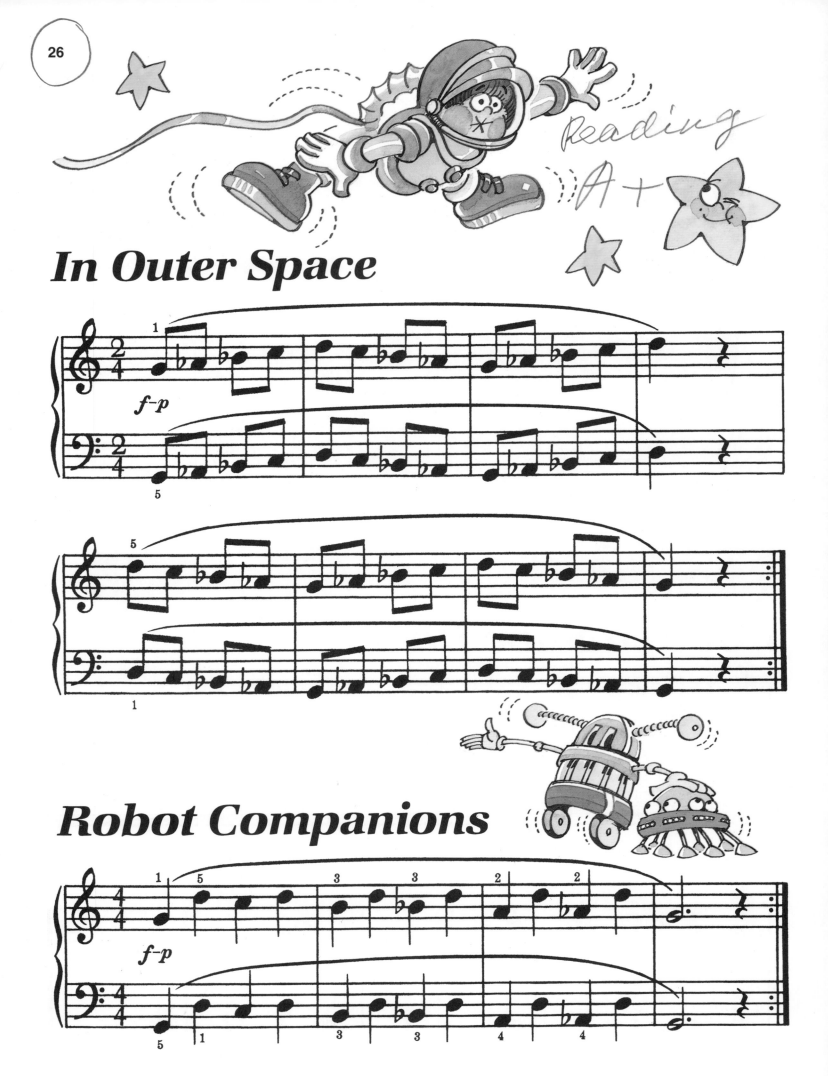

In Outer Space

Robot Companions

Let's Rock!

Begin with a low wrist, and end with a
high wrist for each slurred group.

Phrasing 2's

*Continue this pattern up the keyboard on the white keys.

Phrasing 3's

*Continue this pattern up the keyboard on the white keys.

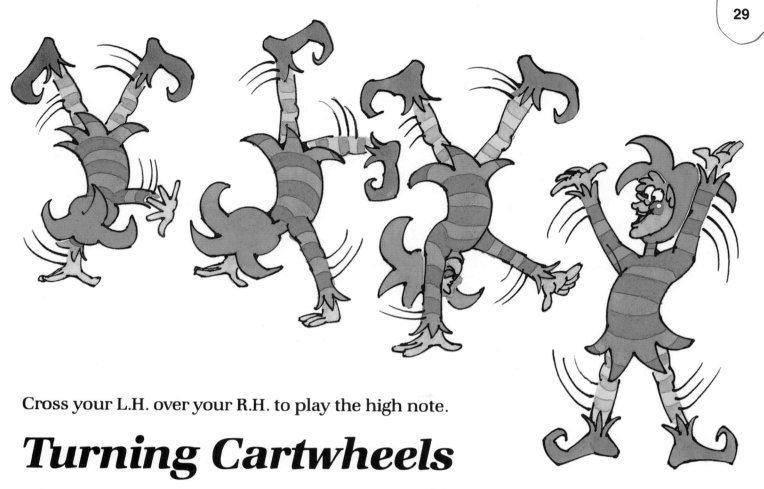

Cross your L.H. over your R.H. to play the high note.

Turning Cartwheels

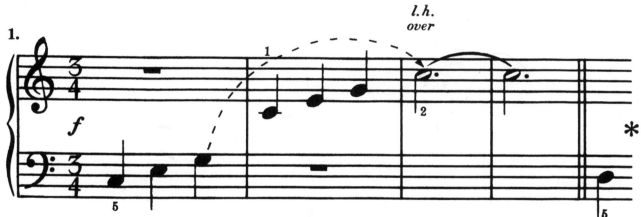

1.

*Continue this pattern up the keyboard on the white keys.

Non legato

2.

*Continue this pattern up the keyboard on the white keys.

Use with page 61 of Piano, Primer Level. **WP215**

The Snake Charmer

1.

*Continue this pattern up the keyboard on the white keys.

2.

*Continue this pattern up the keyboard on the white keys.

Indian Brave

Special Requests for Technic

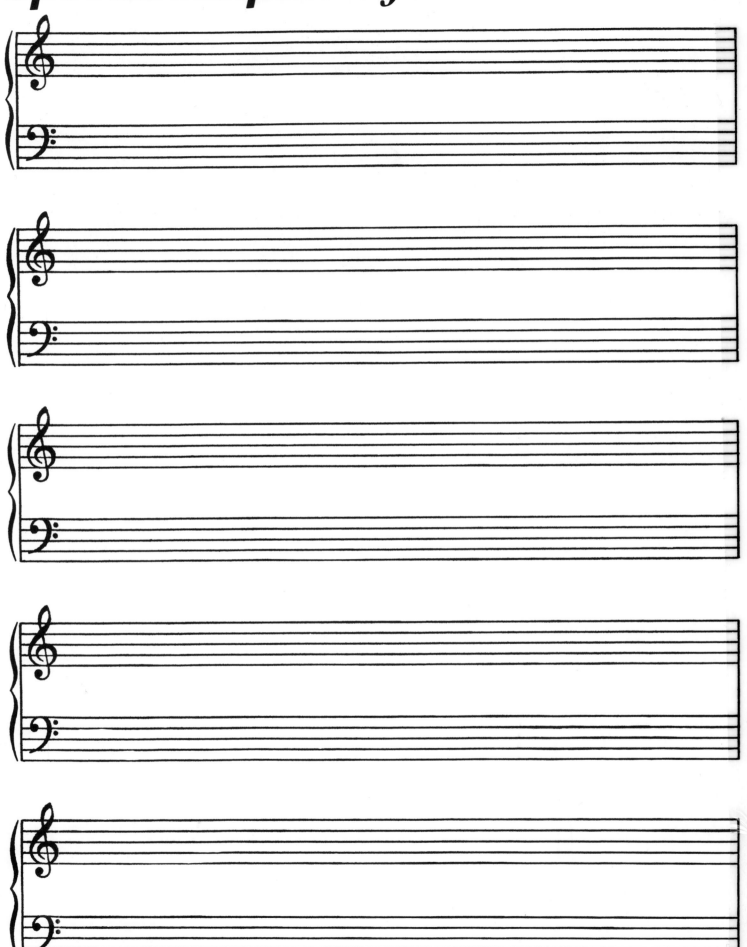